SCIENCE & CHRISTIANITY

PAST, PRESENT, AND FUTURE

Smyth & Helwys Publishing, Inc.
6316 Peake Road
Macon, Georgia 31210-3960
1-800-747-3016

Library of Congress Cataloging-in-Publication Data

CIP information on file

SCIENCE & CHRISTIANITY:

Past, Present, and Future

ᏴᏴᏴᏴ

A GROUP STUDY

D. Andrew Crain, Ph.D.

Professor of Biology | Maryville College

ABOUT THE COVER

The simple sketch of the fish ⟨×, known as the ichthys, has been a symbol for Christians since the second century. During Roman torture of Christians in the first centuries after the crucifixion of Christ, Christians would identify themselves to each other using the ichthys. This symbol originated from an acrostic of the Greek phrase *Iesous Christos Theou Yios Soter*, which translates in English to Jesus Christ, Son of God, Savior.

Today, many more people are familiar with ichthyology, the scientific study of fishes, than the ichthys. The cover illustrates that both the ichthys and ichthyology are important, and both can lead us in the same direction: a direction toward truth.

Photo of fish on cover © Leonardo Gonzalez - stock.adobe.com

SMYTH&HELWYS

PUBLISHING, INCORPORATED ~ MACON, GEORGIA

WWW.HELWYS.COM

FOR MORE INFORMATION

Please visit maryvillecollege.edu/science&christianity

Table of Contents

ooooo

Preface

THIS STUDY GUIDE is derived from a course I teach at Maryville College, Science and Religion, which was initiated by a grant from the Center for Theology and Natural Sciences in the early 2000s and was enhanced by a Calvin College Summer Seminar sponsored by the Issachar Foundation in 2012. A generous grant from TBF Foundation funded compilation of the study guide.

I am indebted to many individuals that have helped with this project. Thoughtful discussions with John Sharp and Mike Hamilton initiated this project. Feedback on drafts was kindly provided by Bill Booth, Jared Crain, Ashlyn Crain, Sally Crain, Gerald Gibson, Lynn Gibson, Mike Hamilton, Randy Hurst, Dan Klingensmith, Bill Meyer, Gary Stinnett, Emerson Wiles, and Mary Wiles. Mary Workman provided graphic design and print production and Brad Coulter of betherecreative.com produced the accompanying YouTube Videos (maryvillecollege.edu/science&christianity).

My wife, Holly, is a constant source of support and joy. I cannot express how much I love her.

Introduction to the Guide

THIS STUDY GUIDE is intended to assist Christian groups to address several modern scientific issues, notably those that seem the most "controversial." A pioneer in the study of science and religion, British physicist and theologian Ian Barbour recognized that one of the most common ways that people characterize the interaction of science and religion is "conflict."[1] However, public and academic libraries are replete with texts addressing "Science and Religion," designated by Dewey Decimal Number 215, and many of these find compatibility, not conflict, between science and faith.[2] Harmony, not conflict, is the consensus of many scientists and theologians,[3] and historian Peter Harrison notes that "…those with more than a passing familiarity with both science and religion have little time for the conflict thesis."[4] One unfortunate truth is that this information rarely finds its way into church doors or Christian study groups, resulting in at least 30% of Americans perceiving a conflict between science and their religious beliefs.[5] Sadly, this conflict narrative can result in people abandoning their faith (particularly younger individuals) or, perhaps as troubling, people of faith dismissing science.

---

[1]   Barbour, I. 1997. *Religion and Science: Historical and Contemporary Issues.* Harper Collins Publisher.

[2]   e.g. Bauer, V.W. 2011. *Can a Christian be an Evolutionist?* 360 pages; Collins, F.S. 2007. *The Language of God: A Scientist Presents Evidence for Belief.* New York: Free Press; Harrison, P. 2010. "Introduction." In *The Cambridge Companion to Science and Religion,* edited by P. Harrison, pg. 16. New York: Cambridge University Press; Noll et al. 2015. *When God and Science Meet: Suprising Discoveries of Agreement.* National Association of Evangelicals; Plantinga, A. 2011. *Where the Conflict Really Lies: Science, Religion, and Naturalism.* Oxford University Press; Polkinghorne, J. 1998. *Science & Theology: An Introduction.* Minnneapolis, MN: Fortress Press; University of California Museum of Paleontology. 2018. *Science and religion: Reconcilable differences.* Accessed February 2, 2018. https://undsci.berkeley.edu/article/science_religion.

[3]   See www.biologos.org

[4]   Harrison, P. (Editor). 2010. *The Cambridge Companion to Science and Religion.* New York: Cambridge University Press. Pg. 16.

[5]   Funk, C. and B.A. Alper. 2015. "Religion and Science." PewResearchCenter: Numbers, Facts and Trends Shaping the World.

It is hoped that this study will provide Christians scriptural considerations and scholarly information on some of the most fundamental, modern scientific concepts (creation, evolution, conservation, and transhumanism) so that both science and faith will be seen as critical components of a flourishing life.[6] This guide is meant to be an instrument for faith communities to become places where scientific engagement is welcome rather than ignored or feared.

This study is divided into 5 sessions, each featuring Bible verses that can be used to provide insight into modern scientific topics and background information on the topics from scientists, theologians, and philosophers that includes numerous references and footnotes if individuals desire more in-depth study. Questions for discussion are provided at the end of each chapter to foster collective learning. Whereas there are no quick or easy answers for topics raised in these sessions, it is hoped that the scientific information provided and scriptures to consider will provide insight.

While an individual could do this study alone, each session is intended to be studied in a group setting. It is recommended that individuals read each chapter prior to the session and then gather for collective discussion and learning. YouTube videos and PowerPoint slides are available if desired.[7]

---

[6] see Volf, M. 2017. *Flourishing: Why We Need Religion in a Globalized World.* Yale University Press.

[7] https://www.maryvillecollege.edu/science&christianity

"*Those who cannot remember the past are condemned to repeat it.*"

∞∞∞ GEORGES SANTAYANA, 1906*

* https://www.iep.utm.edu/santayan

SESSION 1:

Our Historical Landscape: What is Truth?

FOCAL BIBLE VERSES

∞∞ Colossians 2: 8   ∞∞ Psalm 19   ∞∞ John 3: 16–21
∞∞ John 14: 5–7   ∞∞ John 20: 25–27

Introduction

BEFORE WE EXAMINE how modern scientific topics and Christianity interact today, we must first look back at the way that individuals in the Western world have answered one of the fundamental questions that humans have asked: "What is Truth?"

The way that the learned individuals from different eras have answered this question has changed over time, and this is based on time-dependent societal understanding of two ways of knowing: *logos*[1] or *mythos*[2]. *Logos* is the Greek word for reason or plan, and modern-day English derivatives include logic, geology, and biology, whereas *mythos* is Greek for a story having significant truth or meaning and today we derive the English words myth and mythology from *mythos*. "Myth"[3] is often mischaracterized and underappreciated today; however, *mythos* speaks to truth just as much as *logos* does but uses differing means. For example, Table 1.1 presents truths learned through the myths of Aesop's fables.

---

1   *Greek.* The logical reason for something. In contemporary times, the endeavor of *logos* is examined through science.

2   *Greek.* A set of beliefs about something. The framework I use of *mythos* and *logos* is not perfect and is certainly oversimplified, but I believe it is useful nomenclature. Descartes made distinctions between mental and material, and others have used faith and reason.

3   A traditional story that speaks a form of truth, albeit not literally.

TABLE 1.1. *An example of truths learned through the myths of Aesop's fables.*

AESOP FABLE	TRUTH
The Ape and the Fox	Those who aspire to govern must first learn to govern themselves.
The Boy who Cried Wolf	False claims lead to subsequent disbelief.
The Bundle of Sticks	There is strength in unity.
The Dog and the Wolf	Freedom should not be exchanged for comfort or financial gain.
The Fox and the Crow	Accepting false flattery can lead to one's demise.
The Goose that Laid the Golden Eggs	Greed brings demise.
The Grasshopper and the Ant	There is virtue in hard work and planning.
The Lion and the Mouse	Mercy and mutual dependence bring reward.

What is focused on in churches is a mixture of *mythos* and *logos*, but many today have deemphasized the importance of *mythos*. Topics such as the nature of good and evil, rescue and redemption, and the beauty of life itself are themes that can be categorized as *mythos*. This is not to say that the story of God coming to earth in the form of Jesus is only a "myth," as John specifically refers to Jesus as *logos*.[4] Indeed, Christian belief is the perfect example of the unification of *mythos* and *logos* as the two ways of knowing. Christians accept that the most important event that ever occurred on planet Earth is the life, death, and resurrection of Jesus Christ. Whereas the myths of ancient Greece spoke truths through stories that were not real, Jesus Christ spoke and lived the same truths; however, there is one major difference: Jesus walked, talked, and ate both before and after his death. In essence, Jesus was both *logos* and *mythos* simultaneously.

In general, *mythos* and *logos* have had different levels of importance in the following four eras of human history: ancient (~800 B.C. to ~400 A.D.), medieval (~400 A.D. to ~1450 A.D.), modern (~1450-~1945), and postmodern (~1945-present). Figure 1.1 presents a simplification of the changing importance of *mythos* and *logos*. Similar to today, all individuals in each of these eras did

---

4   see John 1: 1.

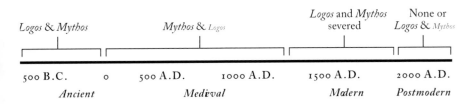

FIGURE 1.1. *Simplified timeline illustrating the way that most individuals defined truth during the ancient, medieval, modern, and postmodern eras.*

not have identical mindsets, but the answer to the question "where do you find truth" has, in general, been characterized differently through human history.

Four Mindsets

ANCIENT

The ancient mindset is characterized by pursuit of truths about both *mythos* and *logos*. We can trace western thought back to the academy in Athens Greece, where truths about meaning and purpose as well as the created world were sought. As an illustration, consider the famous fresco painting by Raphael "The School of Athens," which is located in the Apostolic Palace in the Vatican.[5] In the center of the painting are two figures, one of Plato pointing upward towards the heavens (symbolizing his main focus on *mythos* topics such as ethics, metaphysics, and love) and the other of Aristotle pointing down to the earth (symbolizing his main focus on *logos* topics such as biology, astronomy and meteorology).[6] Aristotle made tremendous strides in study of the natural world, so much so that shortly after his death there was very little examination of nature. Why study the natural world if Aristotle already has the answers to *logos* questions?

Three hundred and fifty years later, Jesus Christ entered planet Earth at a time when humanity craved spiritual direction, desiring truth through *mythos*. But Jesus was not just another prophet like Isaiah or John the Baptist, he was

---

5   see https://www.wikiart.org/en/Search/The%20School%20of%20Athens

6   see http://classics.mit.edu/Browse/index.html ; Aristotle also contributed to philosophical works including ethics.

God in human flesh.[7] As such, one should not expect Jesus to teach on the natural history of the Red Sea or on the age of the Ebenezer stone used by Samuel,[8] yet on how to live a virtuous life both today and eternally. Perhaps Galileo said it best: "… the intention of the Holy Ghost is to teach us how one goes to heaven, not how the heaven goes…"[9]

Based on the typical mindset of those who lived in the first century, it is not unusual that the new testament writers fail to emphasize the natural world. And it at first may seem that Paul discredits study of the natural world. For instance, addressing the church in Colossae, Paul writes

> "See to it that no one takes you captive through hollow and deceptive philosophy, which depends on human tradition and the elemental spiritual forces of this world rather than on Christ."
>
> ∞∞∞ Colossians 2: 8

However, this warning was not about the teachings of Aristotle, but a warning against the teaching of the Gnostics such as astrology.[10] Gnosticism was a 1st and 2nd century threat to early Christianity; it used Christian phrases and tenets to promote a pantheistic belief that the universe was a depraved version of God.[11] Paul wanted to make sure that such a philosophy did not distract early believers from Christ's teachings.

In the few generations after Jesus and Paul, Tertullian emerged as a powerful Christian apologist.[12] Tertullian was particularly interested in the dominance of *mythos*, writing such biting passages as "Now pray tell me,

---

7   see Matthew 1 23, John 10 30-33, John 14 6-7, Philippians 2 5-7, Colossians 2 9, and 1 Timothy 3 16

8   1 Samuel 7-12

9   Galilei, Galileo. 1615. *Letter to the Grand Duchess Christina of Tuscany.* https://web.stanford. edu/~jsabol/certainty/readings/Galileo-LetterDuchessChristina.pdf. pg. 5

10   Barclay, W. 1975. *The Letters to the Phiulippians, Colossians, and Thessalonians.* Revised Edition. Louisville , KY: Westminister John Knox Press.

11   Knight, Kevin. 1909. *Gnosticism.* Accessed July 17, 2018. http://www.newadvent.org/ cathen/06592a.htm.

12   Stanford Encyclopedia of Philosophy Archive. 2016. *History of Trinitarian Docterine.* Accessed May 21, 2018. https://plato.stanford.edu/archives/sum2016/entries/trinity/trinity-history.html#Tertul. Tertullian introduced foundational ideas to our beliefs such as the trinity.

what wisdom is there in this hankering after conjectural speculations?... philosophers; of those, I mean, who persist in applying their studies to a vain purpose, since they indulge a stupid curiosity on natural objects," and "What indeed has Athens to do with Jerusalem? What concord is there between the Academy and the Church?"

In current times, it seems easy to criticize the near-sighted views of those in the ancient world. However, given the fact that in this time period God took human form in Jesus, that Jesus was delivered as the eternal sacrifice for all of humanity, and that death was overcome on the cross, perhaps today we can understand both Paul's and Tertullian's sentiments.

MEDIEVAL

Medieval Christian theology and philosophy was heavily influenced by the writings of Augustine of Hippo in the fifth century. St. Augustine argued that while *mythos* matters are of primary importance, understanding *logos* is also necessary as truths about *logos* can ultimately lead one to spiritual truths. This idea that the natural world can and should be used to ultimately lead to spiritual truths, termed the "handmaiden[13] metaphor," became the theme through the middle ages. Just as Hagar was the handmaid of Sarai and, thus, was used to fulfill Sarai's purpose,[14] the natural world was seen as useful to understanding God.

St. Augustine did not simply see the study of nature and *logos* as a tool to understanding spiritual matters, he took it a step further arguing that willful ignorance of the natural world was detrimental to the spread of Christianity, writing the following:

> "Even a non-Christian knows something about the earth...of the
> years and the seasons, about the kinds of animals, shrubs, stones,
> and so forth, and this knowledge he holds to as being certain from
> reason and experience. Now it is a disgraceful and dangerous thing
> for an infidel to hear a Christian talking nonsense on these topics;

---

13   A subservient person or entity.

14   See Genesis 16: 2-3

and we should take all means to prevent such an embarrassing situation…"[15]

Whereas other ideas, such as those of Tertullian, were bantered about, at the end of the day St. Augustine's dominated. Historian David Lindberg summarizes it this way: "It was Augustine's handmaiden formula, rather than Tertullian's rant, that shaped the relationship between Christianity and the natural sciences through the Middle Ages and beyond."[16] Near the end of the medieval era, theologian Thomas Aquinas supported this handmaiden idea, stating

> "Therefore, the internal acts of religion take precedence of the others and belong to religion essentially, while its external acts are secondary, and subordinate to the internal acts… Religion is the chief of the moral virtues."[17]

The medieval mindset saw *mythos* as of primary importance, but also viewed the truths from *logos* as pointing to God.

MODERN

Following the medieval handmaiden philosophy, the early modern period saw a shift back to the early Ancient mindset of both *logos* and *mythos* being equally important areas of inquiry; both natural and spiritual matters were seen as two distinct books of God. This mindset of truth and beauty being found in both nature and scripture is echoed in Psalm 19:

> The heavens declare the glory of God; the skies proclaim the work of his hands. Day after day they pour forth speech; night after night they reveal knowledge. They have no speech, they use no words; no sound is heard from them. Yet their voice goes out into all the earth, their

---

15 Augustine. 1982. *The Literal Meaning of Genesis: An Unfinished Book.* Translated by J.H. Taylor. Vols. Book 1, Chapter 19, 39. New York: Newman Press.

16 Lindberg, D.C. 2010. "The fate of science in patristic adn medieval Christendom." In *The Cambridge Companion to Science and Religion,* by P. Harrison, 21-38. New York: Cambridge University Press.

17 Aquinas, T. 1920. *The Summa Theologiae.* 2nd and Revised Edition. Translated by Fathers of the English Dominican Province.

words to the ends of the world. In the heavens God has pitched a tent for the sun. It is like a bridegroom coming out of his chamber, like a champion rejoicing to run his course. It rises at one end of the heavens and makes its circuit to the other; nothing is deprived of its warmth.

The law of the Lord is perfect, refreshing the soul. The statutes of the Lord are trustworthy, making wise the simple. The precepts of the Lord are right, giving joy to the heart. The commands of the Lord are radiant, giving light to the eyes. The fear of the Lord is pure, enduring forever. The decrees of the Lord are firm, and all of them are righteous. They are more precious than gold, than much pure gold; they are sweeter than honey, than honey from the honeycomb. By them your servant is warned; in keeping them there is great reward. But who can discern their own errors? Forgive my hidden faults. Keep your servant also from willful sins; may they not rule over me. Then I will be blameless, innocent of great transgression.

May these words of my mouth and this meditation of my heart be pleasing in your sight, Lord, my rock and my redeemer.

∞∞∞ Psalm 19

Freedom of thought that was associated with the scientific revolution coincided with freedom of individual interpretation of scripture.[18] Indeed, most all of the influential scientists in the 16th through 18th centuries examined the natural world because of their faith and contributed significantly to both *logos* and *mythos*. For instance, Francis Bacon (who is attributed with articulating "scientific methodology," also called the "Baconian method") noted that there are

"...two books or volumes to study, if we will be secured from error; first, the Scriptures, revealing the will of God; and then the creatures expressing his power; whereof the latter is a key unto the former."[19]

Historian Peter Harrison goes as far as stating that "the rise of science to

---

18   Harrison, P. 1998. *The Bible, Protestantism, and the Rise of Natural Sciences.* New York: Cambridge University Press.

19   Bacon, F. 1597. *Essays.* London: Digitized by Google.

TABLE 1.2. *Representative early modern "scientists" and their major contributions to both logos and mythos.*

INDIVIDUAL	LIFE	LOGOS CONTRIBUTIONS	MYTHOS CONTRIBUTIONS
Nicolaus Copernicus	1473-1543	Astronomy, Mathematics	Canon law
Francis Bacon	1561-1626	Philosophy, Scientific method	Deductive arguments for God
Johannes Kepler	1571-1630	Astronomy	The Soul
Galileo Galilei	1564-1642	Astronomy, physics	Science and the Bible
Rene Descartes	1596-1650	Mathematics	Innate sense of God, Existence of God
Blaise Pascal	1623-1662	Physics, Geometry	Grace, Free Will
Robert Boyle	1627-1691	Chemistry	Miracles, Existence of God
John Locke	1632-1704	Medicine	Reason and Faith
John Ray	1627-1705	Zoology, Botany,	Natural theology
Isaac Newton	1642-1726	Mathematics, Astronomy, Physics	Miracles and Prophecy
William Paley	1743-1805	Biology	Natural theology

cultural prominence in the eighteenth and nineteenth centuries was possible only because science was eventually able to establish itself as a religiously useful enterprise."[20] To the early modernist, there were two books of knowledge that were important.

But the consilience between faith and reason, between *mythos* and *logos* came to an abrupt end. During the Enlightenment of the 18th century, clear disciplines were solidified. Science became a distinct way of knowing, separate from religion. The unity of *mythos* and *logos* became severed and the two ways of knowing no longer were seen as pointing to the same conclusion.

A second phase in the divorce of *mythos* and *logos* occurred with the industrial revolution. Science shifted from being the process to discern divine order to being the method to master the universe and make money. Thus, by the beginning of the 20th century, the divorce between science and religion was finalized.

---

20   Harrison, P. 2008. "Religion, the Royal Society, and the rise of science." *Theology and Science* 6 (3): 255-271.

POSTMODERN

We currently live in the postmodern era, a time characterized by skepticism of truth. Thus skepticism resulted from the perceived failed aspirations of modernism. The tremendous strides of early modernism and the enlightenment (in fields such as astronomy, chemistry, medicine, and physics) were followed by two world wars and globalism that allowed widespread realization of countless tragedies, religions, and ideas. Is there still truth today and, if so, where can truth be found? Is truth found through science? Is truth found through religion?

Postmodern philosophy accepts "the historicist assumption that reality is an artifact of imaginative, social or political construction."[21] In other words, truth today is perceived by postmodernists as relative and constructed by a particular group of people at a particular place and time. In the contemporary world, the majority of individuals either do not believe in truth (the typical postmodern response) or see science as the primary truth (with religion being used as a handmaiden). And if there is any truth, it is seen to be derived from logos, from Athens. Physicist and priest William Pollard argues against this postmodern perspective when he states:

> "When we look backward over the whole sweep of Western civilization, we cannot move continuously in a single line straight back to ancient Greece. Rather, when we come to the time of our Lord's incarnate life, we must make a distinct branching and thereafter follow independently two distinctive roads into the past: the one leading through Rome to Athens and before, and the other leading through Judah to Israel and before. Western civilization is historically a two-rooted affair...Our basic difficulty is that we live in an age when our whole civilization has in effect lost the capacity to respond to its Judeo-Christian heritage."[22]

"Science" today is defined more narrowly than science in the modern era. Contemporary science has been stripped of philosophy and open inquiry into

---

21   Waters, B. 2016. *From Human to Posthuman: Christian Theology and Technology in a Postmodern World.* New York: Routledge Press.

22   Pollard, W. 1986. *Trancendance and Providence: Reflections of a Physicist and Priest.* Scottish Academic Press. pgs 36 and 40.

existential questions. Whereas in the 17th and 18th centuries "natural history and natural philosophy were frequently pursued from religious motives,"[23] today, science is equated with technology. It has only been in the last 300 years that the concepts of science and religion have emerged as external isolated endeavors instead of as internal virtues.[24] As a result, a 21st century "doctor of philosophy" degree in a scientific field such as chemistry, physics, or biology includes little to no coursework in philosophy, and would be more appropriately termed a "doctor of technology."

Lessons from the Incarnation and the Scientific Disciple

Living in the postmodern era, Christians today are called to show how learning through both *mythos* and *logos* can lead to a flourishing life. As a number of Christian writers have noted, we have a societal responsibility to bring light, beauty, and goodness for the common good.[25] Reflecting back on the different ways that humans have defined truth, it is clear that humanity's greatest strides have occurred when both *logos* and *mythos* were deemed pertinent. Today, fellow believers can reinstall into society such an appreciation for both the natural and the spiritual. Biblical examples that provide touchpoints for conversations about the need for *mythos* and *logos* come both from the incarnation of Jesus and the inquiries of Thomas.

THE INCARNATION

The incarnation of Jesus Christ is the perfect example of the need for appreciation of both *logos* and *mythos*. The word incarnation means the descent from heaven of a god, divine being, or deity into a human or animal form on earth. Most religions include incarnations, but our faith is unique in having the incarnated Jesus not only saving humanity from depravity and death but also reconciling humans to God. For instance, the apostle John writes:

23   Harrison, P. 2006. "Science" and "religion": Constructing the boundaries. *The Journal of Religion* 86 (1), pg. 84

24   Harrison, P. 2015. *The Territories of Science and Religion.* Chicago: The University of Chicago Press.

25   *see* Brueggemann, W. 2010. *Journey to the Common Good.* Louisville, KY: Westminister John Knox Press; Fujimura, M. 2017. *Culture Care: Recommecting with Beauty for Our Common Life.* Dover Grove, IL: Intervarsity Press.

For God so loved the world that he gave his only Son, so that everyone who believes in him may not perish but may have eternal life. Indeed, God did not send the Son into the world to condemn the world, but in order that the world might be saved through him. Those who believe in him are not condemned; but those who do not believe are condemned already, because they have not believed in the name of the only Son of God. And this is the judgment, that the light has come into the world, and people loved darkness rather than light because their deeds were evil. For all who do evil hate the light and do not come to the light, so that their deeds may not be exposed. But those who do what is true come to the light, so that it may be clearly seen that their deeds have been done in God.

∞∞∞ John 3: 16-21

John begins his unique gospel by stating that "In the beginning was the Word, and the Word was with God, and the Word was God. He was with God in the beginning."[26] The English "Word" is translated from the Greek "*Logos*." In other words, the reason for anything is God, who took human form in the body of Jesus. And Christians today believe in this incarnation of God on Earth in the form of Jesus Christ because of Jesus' teachings using *mythos* combined with the reality of his existence and resurrection, the *logos*. Jesus preached the beatitudes. He clarified the law. He healed the lame. He loved those who were shunned. He died on the cross. He rose from the grave three days later. He built a fire. He cooked. He ate. He had Thomas touch his hands and side. Jesus was both body and spirit before and after the Crucifixion. Therefore, God's design is that both *logos* and *mythos* are essential ways of knowing.

THE SCIENTIFIC DISCIPLE

As was mentioned previously, Jesus and the disciples lived at a time when individuals mostly sought truth through *mythos*. However, if there was a most scientific disciple, it was Thomas. Thomas was one of the twelve apostles, is commonly referred to as "doubting Thomas" due to his questioning nature. When Jesus told the disciples that he soon was going to prepare a place for them in heaven

---

26 John 1: 1-2

(see John 14: 1-3), Thomas immediately wants a detailed, scientific explanation.

> Thomas said to him, 'Lord, we don't know where you are going, so
> how can we know the way?" Jesus answered, 'I am the way and the
> truth and the life. No one comes to the Father except through me.
> If you really knew me, you would know my Father as well. From
> now on, you do know him and have seen him.
>
> ∞ John 14: 5-7

It is noteworthy that Jesus' response used both *mythos* (i.e., "I am the way and the truth and the life.") and *logos* (i.e., paraphrased "You see me. I am real. I am God.").

Thomas' scientific mind is shown clearly after the death of Jesus. When confronted with the reality of Jesus' resurrection by some of the other disciples, doubting Thomas stated: "Unless I see the nail marks in his hands and put my finger where the nails were, and put my hand into his side, I will not believe."[27] One week later, Jesus appears to the disciples and immediately goes to Thomas. Jesus does not chastise Thomas, but says "Put your finger here; see my hands. Reach out your hand and put it into my side. Stop doubting and believe."[28] In Thomas, Jesus recognized a *logos* thinker and he did not belittle this. In doing so, Jesus not only lived as the example of both *logos* and *mythos* but he also emphasizes the importance of both modes of seeking truth.

Take Home Message

Throughout human history there have been shifts in the way that the majority of individuals have pursued truth, and the current postmodern mindset views truth as either nonexistent and relative or found in science. However, Christians today can spread light by affirming the generative effects of examining both *mythos* and *logos*. Both scientists and religious leaders have come to this conclusion. For instance, the Harley-riding director of the National Institutes of Health Francis Collins stated

"Science is the way—a powerful way, indeed—to study the natural world.

---

27   John 20: 25

28   John 20: 26-27

Science is not particularly effective—in fact, it's rather ineffective—in making commentary about the supernatural world. Both worlds, for me, are quite real and quite important. They are investigated in different ways. They coexist. They illuminate each other."[29]

and Pope Francis concluded

"Science and religion, with their distinctive approaches to understanding reality, can enter into an intense dialogue fruitful for both."[30]

Questions for Discussion

1. Contemporary Christians have various "mindsets" when it comes to science and faith. For instance, C.S. Lewis yearned for the thinking in the medieval period,[31] whereas U.S. National Institutes of Health Director and evangelical Christian Francis Collins has a perspective of the typical scientist during the early modern period.[32] During which historical era (ancient, medieval, modern, or postmodern) would you say best typifies your mindset?

2. Considering the ideas of Paul and St. Augustine, can both of their ideas be coalesced and consolidated into one "truth?"

3. While it is impossible to project, it is entertaining to postulate what will be the next societal shift in the "Science and Religion" interaction. How do you think people in 2200 will view the topic?

---

29   PBS. 2000. *Religion and Ethics.* Accessed May 25, 2018. http://www.pbs.org/wnet/religionandethics/2000/06/16/transcript-bob-abernethys-interview-with-dr-francis-collins-director-of-the-human-genome-project-at-the-national-institutes-of-health/15204/.

30   Francis, Pope. 2015. *Laudato Si': On Care for our Common Home.* Huntington, IN: Encyclical Letter. pg. 45

31   Lewis, C.S. 1964. *The Discarded Image: An Introduction to Medieval and Renaissance Literature.* Cambridge, England: Cambridge University Press.

32   Collins, F.S. 2007. *The Language of God: A Scientist Presents Evidence for Belief.* New York: Free Press.

"I don't think that there's any conflict at all between science today and the Scriptures. I think we have misinterpreted the Scriptures many times and we've tried to make the Scriptures say things that they weren't meant to say, and I think we have made a mistake by thinking the Bible is a scientific book. The Bible is not a book of science. The Bible is a book of Redemption, and of course, I accept the Creation story. I believe that God created man, and whether it came by an evolutionary process and at a certain point He took this person or being and made him a living soul or not, does not change the fact that God did create man… whichever way God did it makes no difference as to what man is and man's relationship to God."

ооооо BILLY GRAHAM, 1964*

---

* Graham, B., interview by David Frost. 1964. *Doubts and Certainties* BBC-2. Colorado Springs.

SESSION 2:

Creation

FOCAL BIBLE VERSES

∞ Genesis 1: 1–2   ∞ Psalm 89: 5–14   ∞ Psalm 104: 1–5, 24–30
∞ Job 38: 4–11   ∞ John 1: 1–5

Introduction

THE TOPIC OF creation illustrates how a single issue can be viewed
through the different lenses of science and our faith. Science can explain the
"how" of creation, describing the formation of elements from the explosion of
a compacted energy source into billions of solar systems and planets including
our unique Earth. At the same time, any individual that thinks about creation
for any length of time will ask questions such as "Why is there creation in the
first place?" and "Why is there something instead of nothing?" This is where
faith enters the creation conversation. Indeed, creation is broader than nature,
as "it has to do with God's loving plan in which every creature has its own
value and significance."[1]

Understanding Creation from Scriptures

There are many creation stories presented in the Bible, and most people think
of the Genesis 1 and Genesis 2 passages when they think of "creation." We
will study these Genesis creation stories much more in Session 4: Creation
Care, but during the present study we will explore several other, less examined,
creation passages in Job, the Psalms, and the Gospel of John.

Critical to our faith is the idea that God created everything from nothing

---

[1]   Francis, Pope. 2015. *Laudato Si': On Care for our Common Home.* Huntington, IN: Encyclical Letter. p. 54

(*creatio ex nihilio*).[2] This is mentioned many times throughout the Bible, most notably in the opening passages of Genesis. In contrast to pantheistic religions, a major distinction of our faith is the distinction between God and creation; all that is not God was and is created by God.[3]

> In the beginning God created the heavens and the earth. Now the earth was formless and empty, darkness was over the surface of the deep, and the Spirit of God was hovering over the waters.
>
> ∞ Genesis 1: 1–2

Creation depending completely upon God is reiterated in the book of Job. For instance, consider how Yahweh answered some of Job's pointed questions.

> Where were you when I laid the earth's foundation? Tell me, if you understand. Who marked off its dimensions? Surely you know! Who stretched a measuring line across it? On what were its footings set, or who laid its cornerstone—while the morning stars sang together and all the angels shouted for joy? Who shut up the sea behind doors when it burst forth from the womb, when I made the clouds its garment and wrapped it in thick darkness, when I fixed limits for it and set its doors and bars in place, when I said 'This far you may come and no farther; here is where your proud waves halt'?
>
> ∞ Job 38: 4–11

The psalms have much to teach us about the beauty of creation, about our existence, and about the nature of God. Psalm 89 emphasizes that God created everything from nothing and that all of creation depended on God.

> The heavens praise your wonders, O Lord, your faithfulness too, in the assembly of the holy ones. For who in the skies above can compare with the Lord? Who is like the Lord among the heavenly

---

2   *Creatio ex nihilio* is a Latin phrase conveying the idea that all matter came from nothing at the beginning of time. As matter can neither be created nor destroyed (only converted), God is the causative agent for creation.

3   Marvin, J. 2017. "Creation and interpretation. Hermeneutics and the theology of creation." *European Journal of Theology* 26 (1): 43-54. Some theologians believe that creatio ex nihilo was a medieval Christian doctrine, not being an original Jewish or early Christian understanding.

beings? In the council of the holy ones God is greatly feared; he is more awesome than all who surround him. O Lord God Almighty, who is like you? You are mighty, O Lord, and your faithfulness surrounds you. You rule over the surging sea; when its waves mount up, you still them. You crushed Rahab like one of the slain; with your strong arm you scattered your enemies. The heavens are yours, and yours are the earth; you founded the world and all that is in it. You created the north and the south; Tabor and Hermon sing for joy at your name. Your arm is endued with power; your hand is strong, your right hand exalted. Righteousness and justice are the foundation of your throne; love and faithfulness go before you.

∞∞ Psalm 89: 5–14

Simply stated, there is no entity comparable to God, who created everything with love. Humans are not the only entities to acknowledge God's creative power, as the psalmist says that the heavens praise the created wonders!

But creation is not just a historical event; as theologian Ted Peters said: "The act of drawing the world from nonbeing into being is not limited to a once-for-all event in the past. God is doing it right now."[4] Psalm 104 indicates that creation is ongoing and sustained by God. Thus, we should not just view creation as going from nothing to something a long time ago (i.e., *creatio ex nihilo*), but also understand that God's dynamic creation continues (*creatio continua*).[5]

Praise the Lord, O my soul. O Lord my God, you are very great; you are clothed with splendor and majesty. He wraps himself in light as with a garment; he stretches out the heavens like a tent and lays the beams of his upper chambers on their waters. He makes the clouds his chariot and rides on the wings of the wind. He makes winds his messengers, flames of fire his servants. He set the earth on its foundations; it can never be moved...How many are

---

4   Peters, T. 2006. *Anticipating Omega: Science, Faith, and Our Ultimate Future.* Gottingen: Vandenhoeck & Ruprecht. pg. 20

5   *Creatio continua* is Latin for the idea that creation is not only a historical event, but a continuing force in the universe. *See* Bauman, W. 2009. *Theology, Creation, and Environmental Ethics: From Creatio Ex Nihilo to Terra Nullius.* New York: Routledge, Taylor & Francis Group.

your works, O Lord! In wisdom you made them all; the earth is full of your creatures. There is the sea, vast and spacious, teeming with creatures beyond number—living things both large and small. There the ships go to and fro, and the leviathan, which you formed to frolic there. These all look to you to give them their food at the proper time. When you give it to them, they gather it up; when you open your hand, they are satisfied with good things. When you hide your face, they are terrified; when you take away their breath, they die and return to the dust. When you send your Spirit, they are created, and you renew the face of the earth.

∞∞ Psalm 104: 1–5, 24–30

One of the many mystical passages in the New Testament occurs at the beginning of the gospel of John. John is unique among the gospels in the insightful perspective it presents, and John is depicted as "the eagle" in Christian iconography because of his ability to see things from a higher perspective. John's insight is due to his close relationship with Jesus and his ability to understand Christ's relationship to Yahweh.[6]

In the beginning was the Word, and the Word was with God, and the Word was God. He was with God in the beginning. Through him all things were made; without him nothing was made that has been made. In him was life, and that life was the light of men. The light shines in the darkness, but the darkness has not understood it.

∞∞ John 1: 1–5

In summary, the Bible teaches us much about creation, not the "how" of creation, but the "why." The scientific details of creation (i.e., the "how" of creation) cannot be expected to be evident in these ancient texts written thousands of years prior to the advent of science. Theologian Johnathan Marvin summarizes that "the Christian theology of creation asserts the prior gift of meaning within the world and all that derives from this provision."[7] In

---

6   see John 13: 23, 19: 26, 20: 2, 21: 7, and 21: 20

7   Marvin, J. 2017. "Creation and interpretation. Hermeneutics and the theology of creation." *European Journal of Theology* 26 (1): p. 52

other words, scripture teaches us that there is meaning to existence, a meaning that points to God.

Understanding Creation from Science

Science also views "creation" as an ongoing process and not simply a historical event. The origin of matter and the generation of new species are both creation events. Therefore, we will briefly examine both the origin of the universe and the creation of different kinds of organisms.

The scientific understanding of the origin of the universe is still an active area of research, and only in the past 75 years have we been able to articulate a scientific explanation for this creation. Cosmologists (astronomers and physicists working to explain the early history of the cosmos) use astronomical observations and mathematics to reconstruct the earliest origins. Cosmologists have evidence that the universe was once contained in a small mass that exploded and is still expanding, a theory called The Big Bang Theory.[8] This idea was first clearly articulated by a contemporary of Albert Einstein, catholic priest and scientist Georges Lemaître in the 1930s.[9] Based on his study of quantum theory, Lemaître proposed that "we could conceive the beginning of the universe in the form of a unique atom, the atomic weight of which is the total mass of the universe."[10] This idea is consistent with the Christian teaching of *creatio ex nihilo*.

Recent cosmology has shown that the expansion of the universe is accelerating, implying that most of the universe is composed of "dark energy," an unknown energy form that counteracts gravity.[11] Measurements taken

---

8   Big bang theory is the scientific model used to describe the way that the universe came to be, beginning approximately 14 billion years ago as a condensed form of all matter that exploded and continues to expand. Support for this theory comes from Einstein's general theory of relativity, theories of particles, and observations from NASA spacecraft like the Hubble Space Telescope.

9   de Felipe, P. 2017. *Georges Lemaitre, the Scientist and Priest who "Could Conceive the Beginning of the Universe"*. August 23. Accessed March 8, 2018.

10   Lemaître, G. 1931. "The beginning of the world from the point of view of quantum theory." *Nature* 706.

11   Weinberg, S. 2008. *Cosmology*. New York: Oxford University Press. Also, see NASA. 2018. Accessed July 17, 2018. https://science.nasa.gov/astrophysics/focus-areas/what-is-dark-energy.

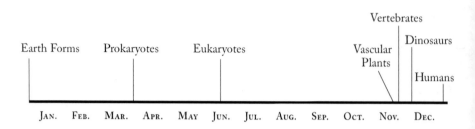

FIGURE 2.1. *Illustration of the 4.5 billion years on earth. If the earth was created on January 1, then humans do not appear until December 31 just before midnight.*

from high-powered telescopes such as the Hubble have calculated the rate of universal acceleration, and the distance measured between galaxies has allowed the age of the universe to be set at 14 billion years before the present.[12]

The Earth and the other planets in our solar system formed about 4.5 billion years ago; data radiometric dating of rocks has scientifically provided this creation date.[13] Four and a half billion years is quite a long time, and understanding creation over this time span is as difficult as understanding the magnitude of the national debt. Thus, it is easier to conceptualize creation of organisms in a single calendar year. If the Earth was created on January 1, then the first eukaryotes (primitive cellular organisms with true organelles including a nucleus) did not appear until mid-summer and humans are not on earth until late on New Year's Eve (see Figure 2.1).

Scientists in the fields of astronomy, physics, mathematics, and biology continue to help explain the mechanisms of historical (*creatio ex nihilo*) and continual (*creatio continua*) creation. But this scientific description cannot enlighten us on

---

12   NASA. *Hubblesite.* Accessed March 8, 2018. http://hubblesite.org/reference_desk/faq/all.php. cat=cosmology.

13   United States Geological Service. 2017. *The Age of the Earth.* April 25. Accessed March 8, 2018. https://geomaps.wr.usgs.gov/parks/gtime/ageofearth.html. Radiometric dating is a technique used to age samples based on the amount of parent and daughter isotopes. In radioactive decay, unstable parent atoms break down to stable daughter atoms at a given rate. For instance, half of Carbon-14 breaks down into Nitrogen-14 in 5,730 years, so if you measured 50% of C-14 and 50% of N-14 in a bone sample, that bone would be 5,730 years old. To date older samples such as igneous rocks, other isotopes with longer "half-lives" are used; half of the original Uranium-235 breaks down to Lead-207 after 704 million years.

why there was and is creation. Astrophysist Robert Jastrow perfectly articulates the failure of science to deliver a complete understanding of creation:

> "At this moment it seems as though science will never be able to raise the curtain on the mystery of creation. For the scientist who has lived by his faith in the power of reason, the story ends like a bad dream. He has scaled the mountains of ignorance; he is about to conquer the highest peak; as he pulls himself over the final rock, he is greeted by a band of theologians who have been sitting there for centuries."[14]

Take Home Message

Both Christianity and science have necessary contributions to the understanding of creation. Our faith provides for us the meaning of creation, whereas modern science explains the "how" questions of creation.

Questions for Discussion

1. Imagine that a non-Christian asks to know what the Bible and your faith teaches you about creation. How do you answer?

2. If creation is not just historical (*creatio ex nihilo*) but also continual (*creatio continua*), what is being continually created?

3. Physicist Ian Barbour wrote that individuals can view particular topics like "Creation" in four different ways: the interaction between the science and the theology can either be in **conflict** (the two are mutually exclusive), **independent** (the two are completely separate ways of knowing), in **dialogue** (both lead to questions that only the other way of knowing can address), or **integrated** (the two ways of knowing are really just part of a single reality). Discuss which of these four you support.

---

14   Jastrow, R. 1978. *God and the Astronomers.* New York: Norton. p. 116

"*There is grandeur in this view of life, with its several powers, having been originally breathed into a few forms or into one; and that, whilst this planet has gone cycling on according to the fixed law of gravity, from so simple a beginning endless forms most beautiful and most wonderful have been, and are being, evolved.*"

∞∞ CHARLES DARWIN, 1859[*]

[*] Darwin, C. 1859. *Origin of Species By Means of Natural Selection, or The Preservation of Favored Races in the Struggle for Life.* New York: D. Appleton and Company. pg. 425.

SESSION 3:

Evolution:
Hindrance or Help?

FOCAL BIBLE VERSES

∞ 2 Timothy 3: 16–17   ∞ Luke 9: 46–48
∞ John 13: 1–5, 12–15   ∞ Philippians 2: 1–11

Introduction

ANY DISCUSSION OF science and faith includes the topic of evolution. A survey by the PewResearchCenter found that of all scientific topics that potentially conflict with Christianity, evolution and Darwin are atop the list.[1] Since Darwin published *On the Origin of the Species* in 1859, Christians have wondered if evolution through natural selection is a hindrance to our faith. During this session, we will first examine the life and ideas of Charles Darwin. After that, we will evaluate if the ideas he proposed provide a challenge to Christian beliefs or if a theology including evolution can actually help us see God more clearly.

Darwin's Story

Many people believe that Charles Darwin is the picture of the atheistic scientist, and it is a common misconception that Darwin's scientific discoveries lead him to atheism. Both of these ideas are not supported. It is true that Darwin died an

---

1   Funk, C. and B.A. Alper. 2015. "Religion and Science." PewResearchCenter: Numbers, Facts and Trends Shaping the World.

agnostic, but the reasons for this stemmed from Darwin's inability to answer a few theological questions with which many people today still struggle.

Charles Robert Darwin was born into an aristocratic family in 1809 in Shrewsbury, England and promptly baptized at the Anglican Parish Church of St. Chad's. When the time came for Darwin to decide on a future career, the obvious choice was to follow in the family tradition of becoming a physician, which was the occupation of his father, grandfather, older brother and uncle. However, Darwin found medical practices in the early 1800s repulsive. Darwin wrote that his father heard that he "did not like the thought of being a physician, so he proposed that I should become a clergyman."[2] While studying to be a parish priest at Cambridge, one of Darwin's professors noted his proclivity for studying animals and plants and arranged for Darwin to be the naturalist on a five-year voyage of the HMS Beagle.[3]

Just as today the websites people frequent indicate their interests, the books that Darwin cherished indicate his intellectual curiosities. While studying to be a clergyman, he was extremely interested in the writings of William Paley. Paley developed the idea of Natural Theology, describing how the complexity seen in living organisms is evidence of a creator (this is called "the watchmaker analogy" or, more broadly, "the design argument").[4] Darwin stated that "The logic of this book and, as I may add, of his Natural Theology gave me as much delight as did Euclid."[5] Another of Darwin's favorite books was *Paradise Lost*, John Milton's Christian classic that attempted to explain the problem of evil, the idea that the existence of pain, suffering, and evil in the world is inconsistent with a loving, all-powerful God.[6]

Upon departing on the H.M.S. Beagle, Darwin was a young 22-year old

---

2   Darwin, C. 2000. *The Autobiography of Charles Darwin.* Edited by Francis Darwin. New York: Prometheus Books. Pg. 17

3   ibid. page 26

4   Natural Theology attempts to provide evidence for God from observed facts and experience. Charles Darwin read and enjoyed William Paley's *Natural Theology, or Evidences of the Existence and Attributes of the Deity Collected from the Appearances of Nature.*

5   Darwin, C. 2000. *The Autobiography of Charles Darwin.* Edited by Francis Darwin. New York: Prometheus Books. Pg. 19

6   Hunter, C.G. 2001. *Darwin's God: Evolution and the Problem of Evil.* Grand Rapids, MI: Brazos Press.

graduate of Christ's College at Cambridge and a student schooled in the mindset of Victorian England. This culture embraced a literal interpretation of virtually all Bible passages.[7] Throughout the voyage, Darwin struggled to remedy the discoveries of geology with the pervasive literal interpretation of Bible stories including the seven-day creation story and the tower of Babel.[8] Sailing around the world experiencing countless civilizations and finding fossils of many extinct species, Darwin recognized that a literal interpretation of much of the book of Genesis was not consistent with his observations, and he questioned the Victorian concept of "God-breathed" being interpreted as literal and infallible.[9] Today many understand God-breathed as God-inspired instead of as literal truth.[10] However, a product of his Victorian culture, "Darwin viewed the rejection of his previous belief in the literal truth of every biblical verse as a diminution of his faith, not as an enlargement of it."[11] Thus, a literal interpretation of all scriptures led Darwin to question his faith.

Whereas some of Darwin's doubts stemmed from the pervasive culture-based literal interpretation of scripture, Darwin's major struggle was to understand how a loving God could allow pain and suffering.[12] In 1851, the tragic loss of his ten-year-old daughter Annie left Darwin in deep despair and solidified his agnostic stance. Darwin said that through Annie's death, he had "lost the joy of the household, and the solace of our old age."[13] Explanations

---

7   Wood, L.W. 2005. *Theology as History and Hermeneutics.* Lexington, KY: Emeth Press. Wood states that "literalism is the legacy of Kantianism." Pg. 29. Interestingly, this Biblical literalism occurred simultaneous with the scientific revolution.

8   Ruse, M. 2008. *Charles Darwin.* Malden, MA: Blackwell Publishing.

9   Darwin's ideas were similar to the ideas of St. Augustine, see Session 1.

10   Read 2 Timothy 3: 16-17 and consider how the phrase "God-breathed" can be interpreted differently. Does "God-breathed" mean that we are to read all scriptures as literal? Today, 39% of U.S. Christians say that the Bible's text should be taken literally, whereas 36% believe it should not (see http://www.pewresearch.org/fact-tank/2017/04/14/5- facts-on-how-americans-view-the-bible-and-other-religious-texts/.) Thus, there is more variation in the way that scriptures are interpreted than in the time of Darwin.

11   Phipps, W.E. 2002. *Darwin's Religious Odyssey.* Harrisburg, PA: Trinity Press International. pg. 31.

12   Phipps, W.E. 2002. *Darwin's Religious Odyssey.* Harrisburg, PA: Trinity Press International.

13   University of Cambridge. n.d. *Darwin Correspondence Project.* Accessed June 14, 2018. https://www.darwinproject.ac.uk/people/about-darwin/family-life/death-anne-elizabeth-darwin.

for the problem of evil have evolved much over time,[14] and the 19th century ideas were not sufficient to answer Darwin's questions. One is left to wonder that if Darwin were alive today he would be a believer because of modern conceptions of theodicy. For example, when Pope Francis was asked why God would allow children to suffer, he answered:

> "Quite simply, because He created us as persons and as such free. God is respectful of human freedom. He allowed his son to be killed on the cross. [In] the game of human freedom, God risked a lot here! It would more dishonor man if God could take away his freedom than if man, with his freedom, committed a crime."[15]

Late in his life, Darwin was very private in religious matters, stating that the best description of his belief system was agnosticism. Darwin questioned the existence of God, but he certainly did not refute the existence of God. Like many today, Darwin had questions, illustrated by this quote:

> "I may state that my judgment often fluctuates…In my most extreme fluctuations I have never been an atheist in the sense of denying the existence of a God. I think that generally (and more and more as I grow older), but not always, that an agnostic would be the more correct description of my state of mind."[16]

In summary, Darwin's scientific insights did not lead him away from God. Darwin himself admitted that his agnosticism was not due to his scientific epiphanies, as indicated in his 1871 correspondence to an editor that asked Darwin to submit an article on how his idea of natural selection impacts religion and morality. Darwin declined the offer, stating:

> "I have never systematically thought much on religion in relation to science, or on morals in relation to society; and without steadily

---

14   Hicks, J. 2010. *Evil and the God of Love*. London: Palgrave Macmillan.

15   Wenders, W. 2018. Pope Francis—A Man of His Word. Documentary film.

16   2000. *The Autobiography of Charles Darwin*. Edited by Francis Darwin. New York: Prometheus Books. Pg. 59.

keeping my mind on such subjects for a long period, I am really incapable of writing anything worth sending."[17]

Darwin's Theory of Natural Selection

One common misconception is that the term "theory" means that there are other equally supported explanations. However, in science a theory is not simply a conjecture. A scientific theory is defined as an explanation that has been overwhelmingly supported by numerous scientific studies. For instance, in the early 1800s, several scientists proposed the idea that many diseases are caused by microorganisms such as bacteria and viruses. This hypothesis was supported in numerous experiments through the mid 1800s, resulting in today's "germ theory." Another theory we have today is cell theory, the idea that all living organisms are composed of cells. The theory of natural selection is just as supported as germ and cell theory. Let us briefly examine the theory of natural selection.

Charles Darwin collected exhaustive amounts of fossils, artifacts, and notes during the voyage of the H.M.S. Beagle from 1831-1836. For the following two decades, Darwin examined and considered his observations and finally published *Origin of Species*, where he outlined the way that populations and species (but not individuals) change over time.[18] In this 1859 publication, Darwin outlined this evolutionary process that he called natural selection:

1. Individuals in a population vary in their traits

2. Variations in these traits are inherited from parents

3. More offspring are produced than can survive

4. The offspring that survive in a particular environment reproduce, thus passing on their traits to the next generation

---

17   Darwin, 2000. *The Autobiography of Charles Darwin.* Edited by Francis Darwin. New York: Prometheus Books. Pg. 60.

18   Darwin, C. 1901. *Origin of Species By Means of Natural Selection, or The Preservation of Favored Races in the Struggle for Life.* New York: P.F. Collier and Son .

Darwin's theory challenged the natural theology of the late 1800s that was attempting to provide evidence of God through the design argument.[19] Natural selection provided a mechanism that eliminated the need for God as the designing agent. At the same time, Darwin recognized that in the early 1800s a belief in "pervading spiritual agencies seems to be universal."[20] Some modern theologians claim that Darwin was a theist in search of a better, more complete theism, namely, one that could understand God and the world in evolutionary terms.[21] But because theology had not yet caught up to Darwin's evolutionary insights, he became increasingly agnostic. Indeed, a richer theology was developed as a result of Darwin's theory.

A Theology Including Evolution

Since Darwin published *On the Origin of the Species* in 1859, Christians have wondered if evolution through natural selection is a hindrance or help to our faith. Three questions arising from the theory of natural selection are: (1) Does natural selection give a better explanation for the existence of pain and suffering than the theodicy?, (2) Does natural selection mean that humans are not the reason for creation?, and (3) Does natural selection remove purpose and meaning from creation? While these are challenging questions, theologian John Haught contends that a theology including evolution can give us more insight into the nature of God.

> "But we shall see that Darwin's portrayal of the way the universe works actually invites us to think about God, once again, in a meaningful and truly inspiring way."[21]

19 Brooke, J.H. 2003. "Darwin and Victorian Christianity." In *The Cambridge Companion to Darwin*, edited by J. and G. Radick Hodge, 192-213. New York: Cambride University Press.

20 Darwin, C. 1871. *The Descent of Man and Selection in Relation to Sex.* London: John Murray. pg. 394

21 Haught, J. 2008. *God after Darwin: A Theology of Evolution.* 2nd Edition. Boulder, CO: Westview Press. pg. 24

Pain and Suffering: The Problem of Theodicy

The problem of pain and suffering asks how an all-powerful (omnipotent), all-knowing (omniscient), and all-loving (omnibenevolent) God could allow so many bad things in this world. There have been many books written for Christians to help understand this topic, termed "theodicy" (including seminal works by C.S. Lewis[22] and Philip Yancey[23]), and there is certainly no simple answer to the problem of evil.

One of the early and persistent oppositions to Darwin's theory was the worry that natural selection provided a mechanism that explained both creation and pain and suffering that did not rely on the hand of God. Darwin's theory of natural selection did not threaten God's existence as the initiator of all creation, but did provide another explanation for controlling the life or death of organisms. For instance, if the naturalistic explanation of creation of individuals and species necessarily results in harm and death of weaker individuals, then questions of the theodicy are irrelevant as God is removed from the equation. In summary, Elohim God[24] was replaced by a natural process. However, this may be a near-sighted viewpoint that is based on the way that most Christians wish to view God.

A tenable solution to the problem of pain and suffering is to reconsider our understanding of God, viewing God as humble and sharing in the suffering of creation instead of as a conqueror. Just as through the ages individuals have sought truth differently (see Session 1), human conceptions of God have evolved as well. Early Christians viewed God as omnipotent but humble and vulnerable. This viewpoint changed to a more imperial view of God as Christianity was introduced to the West.[25] Theologian John Haught summarizes it this way:

> "When Christianity entered Western culture, as Alfred North Whitehead

---

22   Lewis, C.S. 1996. *The Problem of Pain.* New York: Touchstone Press.

23   Yancey, P. 1990. *Where is God When it Hurts?* Grand Rapids, MI: Zondervan Press.

24   Jewish Encyclopedia. 1906. *The unedited full-text of the 1906 Jewish Encyclopedia.* Accessed June 11, 2018. http://www.jewishencyclopedia.com/articles/5704-elohim.

25   Haught, J. 2008. *God after Darwin: A Theology of Evolution.* 2nd Edition. Boulder, CO: Westview Press.

rightly indicates, the image of Caesar rather than that of the humble
shepherd of Nazareth became the regnant model of God...However, the
ancient Christian sense of God's humility and vulnerability has begun
to emerge more explicitly once again in contemporary theology."[26]

The Jews wished for an imperialist messiah riding on a powerful stallion
instead of a young donkey, and it seems many Christians do as well.

However, this concept of God as an imperialist conqueror is not consistent
with Biblical teachings. Scriptures teach that God is self-limiting and suffering
with creation, and no study guide would be long enough to discuss the humble,
vulnerable, selfless nature of Jesus Christ. As a few examples, consider the words
and actions of Jesus as well as the ideas of Paul in the following scriptures:

> An argument started among the disciples as to which of them
> would be the greatest. Jesus, knowing their thoughts, took a
> little child and had him stand beside him. Then he said to them,
> "Whoever welcomes this little child in my name welcomes me; and
> whoever welcomes me welcomes the one who sent me. For he who
> is least among you all—he is the greatest.
>
> ∞∞∞ Luke 9: 46-48

It was just before the Passover Feast. Jesus knew that the time had come for
him to leave this world and go to the Father. Having loved his own who were
in the world, he now showed them the full extent of his love.

> The evening meal was being served, and the devil had already
> prompted Judas Iscariot, son of Simon, to betray Jesus. Jesus knew
> that the Father had put all things under his power, and that he had
> come from God and was returning to God; so he got up from the
> meal, took off his outer clothing, and wrapped a towel around his
> waist. After that, he poured water into a basin and began to wash
> his disciples' feet, drying them with the towel that was wrapped
> around him...

---

26   ibid. pg. 52

When he had finished washing their feet, he put on his clothes
and returned to his place. 'Do you understand what I have done
for you?' he asked them. 'You call me "Teacher" and "Lord,"
and rightly so, for that is what I am. Now that I, your Lord and
Teacher, have washed your feet, you also should wash one another's
feet. I have set you an example that you should do as I have done
for you.

∞∞ John 13: 1-5, 12-15

If you have any encouragement from being united with Christ, if
any comfort from his love, if any fellowship with the Spirit, if any
tenderness and compassion, then make my joy complete by being
like-minded, having the same love, being one in spirit and purpose.
Do nothing out of selfish ambition or vain conceit, but in humility
consider others better than yourselves. Each of you should look not
only to your own interests, but also to the interests of others.

Your attitude should be the same as that of Christ Jesus: Who being
in very nature God, did not consider equality with God something
to be grasped, but made himself nothing, taking the very nature
of a servant, being made in human likeness. And being found in
appearance as a man, he humbled himself and became obedient to
death—even death on a cross! Therefore, God exalted him to the
highest place and gave him the name that is above every name, that
at the name of Jesus every knee should bow, in heaven and on earth
and under the earth, and every tongue confess that Jesus Christ is
Lord, to the glory of God the Father.

∞∞ Philippians 2: 1-11

In summary, Christ's humility and suffering gives us a view of God
that is the opposite of an imperialist leader. This does not discount God's
omnibenevelence and omniscience, as our self-limiting God suffers with us
through times of pain, providing comfort and support. Thus, evil is present,
but God suffers with all creatures and this is not in opposition to the scientific
observations supporting the theory of natural selection.

The Role of Humans in Creation

Another challenge that the theory of natural selection poses is our concept of the role of humans. Just as we wish to view God as an all-powerful imperialist, Christians have long viewed humans as the pinnacle of all creation. But Darwin's ideas challenge this, positing that humans are simply another of the numerous products of natural selection. If this is true, then the purpose of creation is not just about humans. One response to this anthropocentric view is to discount Darwin's theory, but another is to reconsider our human-centered view.

It is certainly true that humans were uniquely created, as the Bible states that we were made special among all creatures. For instance:

> Then God said, "Let us make mankind in our image, in our likeness, so that they may rule over the fish in the sea and the birds in the sky, over the livestock and all the wild animals, and over all the creatures that move along the ground. So God created mankind in his own image, in the image of God he created them; male and female he created them.
>
> ∞∞∞ Genesis 1: 26-27

Humans have cognitive abilities that are unique among all creatures, abilities that characterize us as being made in the image of God. Simply stated, humans are an animal, but we are not just any animal. The specialness that we have is that we are called upon by God to be stewards of creation, a topic that will be thoroughly explored in Session 5. However, scriptures do not claim that we are the purpose of creation.

After Darwin, the human-centered nature of God was challenged, opening up the idea that, even though we are special in creation, "an evolutionary theology, it goes without saying, expands this picture of God's suffering so as to have it embrace also the struggles of the entire universe and not just our own species' brief history here."[27] If we do not view humans as the purpose of creation, then natural selection is not a threat to Christianity.

---

27   ibid. pg. 55

Purpose, Beauty, and Value

A common misconception is that Darwinian evolution implies a purposeless existence, but the theory of natural selection is completely neutral on the topic of whether there is something beyond the natural. While it is true that many contemporary scientists do not believe in God, this has nothing to do with "science" but their belief system called "naturalism."[28] Naturalism is the philosophy that there is nothing beyond natural phenomena, that everything can be explained by and is the result of science, including world religions.[29] Some, but certainly not all, scientists believe in naturalism, with at least 40% of U.S. scientists believing that God has a guiding hand in evolution.[30] Sociologist Elaine Ecklund has discovered that it is not science that weakens scientists' faith, as the strongest predictor of faith as an adult in scientists is religiosity in the home when the scientist was a child.[31] After understanding that evolution does not imply a meaningless and purposeless existence, natural selection can be seen as a beautiful process that makes creation an ongoing phenomenon.

Evolution through natural selection is the mechanism of continual creation. As discussed in Session 2, creation should not only be viewed historical event at the beginning of time, but also as a continual process (creatio continua). Natural selection has created and will continue to create beauty among all life forms.

A colleague of mine, ethicist and theologian William Meyer, argues that Darwin himself not only acknowledged beauty in nature, but he also assumed

---

28 Plantinga, A. 2011. *Where the Conflict Really Lies: Science, Religion, and Naturalism.* Oxford University Press. Naturalism describes a belief system where everything is attributed to natural causes and all supernatural explanations are excluded. The term materialism is often used as a synonym of naturalism, basically positing that all that exists is matter.

29 see Wilson, D.S. 2002. *Darwin's Cathedral: Evolution, Religion, and the Nature of Society.* Chicago: The University of Chicago Press. & Wilson, E.O. 1999. *Consilience: The Unity of Knowledge.* New York: Vintage Books.

30 Witham, L. 1997. *Many Scientists See God's Hand in Evolution.* April 11. Accessed April 11, 2018. https://ncse.com/library-resource/many-scientists-see-gods-hand-evolution. Also, see http://www.pbs.org/wgbh/evolution/religion/faith/index.html to see how many leading biologists, biochemists, physicists and historians of science respond to the numerous questions arising from an understanding of Darwinian evolution.

31 Ecklund, E.H. and C.P. Scheitle. 2007. "Religion among academic scientists: Distinctions, Disciplines, and Demographics." *Social Problems* 54 (2): 289-307.

the existence of value in the natural world, and this is certainly not the "meaninglessness" that some contemporary materialists describe in evolution.[32] Thus, Darwinian evolution not only describes the mechanism of passing on traits to future generations by survival and reproduction, but also assumes a teleology of value (in contrast to a teleology of design, which Darwin explicitly rejected). In other words, Darwin viewed humans and other species (such as birds) as pursuing value in the world in the form of beauty and other forms of worth.

Take Home Message

In summary, the ideas of Charles Darwin are not in conflict with Christian beliefs. Darwin's personal faith story is sad, and the struggles he faced are still faced by people today. A theology including evolution shows that our creator and savior God holds all of creation in his hands, and He suffers with creation. Natural selection is the mechanism of continual creation, creating the beauty that we see in the natural world.

Questions for Discussion

1. In the U.S., Charles Darwin is often vilified for his ideas. Why do you think this is?

2. Do Darwin's two major problems with Christianity (biblical literalism and the problem of evil) trouble you? Many non-Christians have reservations based on these same issues today. How should we respond to these issues?

3. Is it possible for God to be self-limiting and vulnerable, yet still all-powerful?

4. Do you believe that evolution through natural selection eliminates purpose and meaning?

---

32   Meyer, W.J. 2016. *Darwin in a New Key: Evolution and the Question of Value.* Eugene, OR: Cascade Books.

"A thing is right when it tends to preserve the integrity, stability and beauty of the biotic community. It is wrong when it tends otherwise."

∞∞∞ A<small>LDO</small> L<small>EOPOLD</small>, 1949 [*]

[*] Leopold, A. 1966. *A Sand County Almanac (Outdoor Essays & Reflections)*. The Random House Publishing Company. pg. 262

SESSION 4:

Creation Care:
Redemption of the Land

FOCAL BIBLE VERSES

∞∞ Genesis 1: 1-2:3   ∞∞ Genesis 2: 15   ∞∞ Leviticus 25: 23-24

∞∞ Mark 12: 29-30   ∞∞ Romans 8: 19-23

Introduction

EVERY AMERICAN SCHOOL child today is familiar with the history
of environmental degradation and the need for sustainability, and the Bible
speaks clearly of the earth's beauty and our responsibility to protect it.
Christians today need to know how to respond to contemporary environmental
issues in a Biblical manner, and if we do not address these issues, many young
people will find the teachings of the church irrelevant.

The Importance of Creation Care to our Faith

The need for God's people to care for the land has been acknowledged since
the beginning of farming.[1] As the writer of Leviticus says, when we use
the land, we must "provide redemption of the land."[2] That the land needs
"redemption" seems odd at first to western eyes, but this is likely due to the
self-centered view that westernized Christianity has taken. Today's churches

---

1   Genesis 2: 15

2   see Leviticus 25: 23-25

struggle to stay "relevant" to the whims of their parishioners because the alternative is empty pews or portable chairs. Such self-centeredness in Christianity is nothing new, as this perspective has allowed believers to subconsciously ignore or justify some of the worst acts of humanity including slavery, sexual exploitation of children, abandonment of the elderly and, now, environmental destruction.[3] The time has come for Christians to shun such self-centeredness. Anyone reading the New Testament will note that the teachings of Christ were the opposite of self-centeredness, and a Christ-centered life today should be characterized by a healthy relationship with God, with others, and with creation.

Most readers will heartily agree that a healthy relationship with God is pertinent and a healthy relationship with others necessary. Indeed, when Christ was asked "Of all the commandments, which is the most important?" he answered:

> The most important one, answered Jesus, is this: 'Hear, O Israel: The Lord our God, the Lord is one. Love the Lord your God with all your heart and with all your soul and with all your mind and with all your strength.' The second is this: 'Love your neighbor as yourself.' There is no commandment greater than these.
>
> ∞∞∞ Mark 12: 29-30

But what is the justification for a Christ-centered life also focusing on a healthy relationship with creation? Simply stated, there is a creation care mandate presented through the entire Bible.

The goodness and beauty of creation are presented in the first creation story (Genesis 1: 1, 2: 3). Much can be learned from this passage, as it teaches us that God created all things, but not all agency was directly from God as the earth brought forth vegetation and the waters were invited to bring forth living creatures. Additionally, creation is seen as good and the earth is here for all creatures, not just humans. Indeed, humans are not the climax of creation, but the Sabbath is.[4] Combined reading of the first (Gen. 1: 1– 2: 3) and second

---

3   Francis, Pope. 2015. *Laudato Si': On Care for our Common Home.* Huntington, IN: Encyclical Letter.

4   Bouma-Prediger, S. 2010. *For the Beauty of the Earth: A Christian Vision for Creation Care.* 2nd Edition. Grand Rapids, MI: Baker Academic Press.

(Gen. 2: 4-25) creation stories in Genesis show Christians "that human life is grounded in three fundamental and closely intertwined relationships: with God, with our neighbor and with the earth itself."[5] Climate scientist Katharine Hayhoe states this in a slightly different way, saying that our faith calls for creation care because of (1) our love for others, (2) our love for God and his creation, and (3) our acknowledgement of creation as a gift from God.[6] In other words, our relationship with God, others, and creation are all connected, and a healthy relationship with all three should be sought. Creation care is not simply a reaction to a fallen world, but it is a tenant of our faith.

The Psalms are full of praises for the beauty of the natural world[7] and even Job saw creation's beauty during his distress,[8] but it was Paul that was very clear that preservation of this beautiful creation is the responsibility of Christians, who he calls "the sons of God"[9]:

> The creation waits in eager expectation for the sons of God to be revealed. For the creation was subjected to frustration, not by its own choice, but by the will of the one who subjected it, in hope that the creation itself will be liberated from its bondage to decay and brought in to the glorious freedom of the children of God. We know that the whole creation has been groaning as in the pains of childbirth right up to the present time.
>
> ∞∞∞ Romans 8: 19-23

Today, Paul's desire for the earth to be liberated from its bondage to decay is termed conservation by scientists and creation care by people of faith. A Christian "environmental ethic" that is predicated on stewardship of the land

---

5   Francis, Pope. 2015. *Laudato Si': On Care for our Common Home.* Huntington, IN: Encyclical Letter. Pg. 47

6   Hayhoe, D. 2017. "Creation as a gift: A neglected approach to creation care." *Science and Christian Belief* 29: 93-120.

7   e.g., Psalm 24: 1, Psalm 84: 1-7, Psalm 104: 31, Psalm 148: 3-4

8   Job 12: 1-10

9   Just before the focal passage, Paul defines the "sons of God" as those who are led by the Spirit of God. See Romans 8: 14

has been called for by both scientists and theologians,[10] and this issue is not one isolated to any particular Christian denomination. The universal Christian acceptance of the need for our acknowledgement of creation care is illustrated in the following quotes from John Calvin and Pope Francis.

> "Let him who possesses a field...endeavor to hand it down to posterity as he received it, or even better cultivated...let every one regard himself as the steward of God in all things which he possesses.[11]
>
> ∞∞∞ John Calvin

> "The ultimate purpose of other creatures is not to be found in us. Rather, all creatures are moving forward with us and through us towards a common point of arrival, which is God, in that transcendent fullness where the risen Christ embraces and illumines all things. Human beings, endowed with intelligence and love, and drawn by the fullness of Christ, are called to lead all creatures back to their Creator."[12]
>
> ∞∞∞ Pope Francis

Christians today must affirm the importance of environmental stewardship as a component of faith development. The first step in creation care is acknowledgement of the current ecological crisis and how we arrived there and the second is to work towards solutions. As writer and farmer Wendell Berry states, we should

---

10   e.g., Bouma-Prediger, S. 2010. *For the Beauty of the Earth: A Christian Vision for Creation Care.* 2nd Edition. Grand Rapids, MI: Baker Academic Press; Bergstrom, J.C. 2014. *What the Bible Says About the Environment.* November 14. Accessed February 15, 2018. https://arcapologetics.org/culture/subdue-earth-bible-says-environment/; Hayhoe, D. 2017. "Creation as a gift: A neglected approach to creation care." *Science and Christian Belief* 29: 93-120; White, L.W. 1967. "The historical roots of our ecologic crisis." *Science* 155: 1203-1207.

11   Calvin, J. Commentary on Genesis. Accessed March 9, 2018. https://www.iclnet.org/pub/resources/text/m.sion/calvgene.htm.

12   Francis, Pope. 2015. *Laudato Si': On Care for our Common Home.* Huntington, IN: Encyclical Letter. pg. 58

"cherish hope for the success of compassion, mercy, forgiveness, neighborly love, responsible freedom, and the loving care of the earth that all of those goods imply, but the success of that hope is only endangered by ignoring our record of costs and losses."[13]

The Status of Earth's Groaning

We can track the costs and losses of environmental health in the U.S. back to the arrival of westerners in the new world. European colonists interpreted "subduing the earth" in Genesis 1: 28 quite literally, leading to a habit of environmental degradation through the 19th and 20th centuries.[14] But this idea of subduing nature is only mentioned once in the Bible, whereas stewardship of nature is mentioned many times, and today we recognize that dominion does not necessarily connote destruction. By the mid 20th century, industrialization had led to widespread environmental destruction, which promoted societal response for environmental health. For instance, consider the following ideas of Christian author and medieval scholar C.S. Lewis and marine biologist and Silent Spring author Rachel Carson:

"No doubt those who really founded modern science were usually those whose love of truth exceeded their love of power…[But] its triumphs may have been too rapid and purchased at too high a price: reconsideration, and something like repentance, may be required,"

∞∞∞ C.S. Lewis, 1943 [15]

"How could intelligent beings seek to control unwanted species by a method that contaminated the entire environment and brought

---

13 Berry, W. 2017. *The Art of Loading Brush: New Agrarian Writings*. Berkeley, CA: Counterpoint Press. pg. 67

14 Page, C.M. 2007. *American Environmental Hisotry: An Introduciton*. New York: Columbia University Press.

15 Lewis, C.S. 1996. "The Abolition of Man." *In The Essential C.S. Lewis*, by C.S. Lewis, edited by L.W. Dorsett, 536 . New York: Simon & Schuster Publisher.pg. 457

the threat of disease and death even to their own kind? Yet this is precisely what we have done."

∞∞∞ Rachel Carson, 1962[16]

The story is certainly not all bad, for as a result of social influence, the 1970s saw much environmental clean-up due to governmental action. The Environmental Protection Agency was established in 1970, and numerous congressional acts for environmental health were passed, including the Environmental Quality Improvement Act, Safe Drinking Water Act, the Endangered Species Act, the Toxic Substances Control Act.[17] Whereas in the 1960s, the Cuyahoga river in Ohio burned from petroleum pollution and a school was built on a hazardous waste site at Love Canal in New York, the late 20th century saw improvements in a few environmental endpoints in the U.S. The percent of forested land in the US, which were being destroyed in the 18th and 19th centuries at epidemic proportions, stabilized in the 20th century,[18] and the amount of some toxicants have declined in children's blood (for instance, blood lead levels have fallen precipitously since the 1970s).[19]

However, we have now entered a new geologic era that scientists refer to as the Anthropocene, which is marked by human activity as the key determinant in geological, biological and ecological processes (including climate).[20] Due to the increase in human population and fossil fuel use, scientists around the globe now note that most indicators of environmental health have declined and are declining at a rapid rate. At an all-time low are freshwater resources, vertebrate

---

16   Carson, R. 1962. *Silent Spring*. Boston: Houghton Mifflin Company. pg. 8-9

17   Klaassen, C. 2007. *Casarett & Doull's Toxicology: The Basic Science of Poisons*. 7th Edition. Portland: McGraw-Hill Professionial.

18   U.S. Forest Service. 2001. "U.S. Forest Facts and Historical Trends." FS-696-M, U.S. Department of Agriculture, 24.

19   see Spivey, A. 2007. "The weight of lead: Effects add up in adults." *Environmental Health Perspectives* 115 (1): A30-A36 ; However, there is no safe level of lead in children. Centers for Disease Control and Prevention. 2017. Lead. December 4. Accessed February 16, 2018. https://www.cdc.gov/nceh/lead/.

20   NASA. 2013. *The Anthropocene: Humankind as a Turning Point for Earth*. June 27. Accessed April 27, 2018. https://astrobiology.nasa.gov/news/the-anthropocene-humankind-as-a-turning-point-for-earth/.\

species abundance, and total forest area, whereas the number of marine areas with no life (called "dead zones"), CO_2 emissions and the associated global temperature are increased (see Figure 4.1).[21] More than 15,000 scientists from 184 countries summarize that "by failing to adequately limit population growth, reassess the role of an economy rooted in growth, reduce greenhouse gasses, incentivize renewable energy, protect habitat, restore ecosystems, curb pollution, halt defaunation, and constrain invasive alien species, humanity is not taking the urgent steps needed to safeguard our imperiled biosphere."[22]

Providing the Land Redemption

The idea that Christians can influence the Earth's deteriorating health at first seems overwhelming, but theologian N.T. Wright said it best: "Despite all, there is hope."[23] The first step in promoting creation care is to acknowledge that our faith is not about us (it is not anthropocentric), but it is about God (it is theocentric). God provides us redemption through his grace, and we are called to be the agents of redemption for creation. But specifically, how?

Numerous individual and Christian-community based actions can improve environmental health. Whereas large-scale, wide-spread actions are attractive, the most effective solutions can be produced at the local level. The popular phrase "think globally, act locally" is appropriate for Christians. Local church-led environmental projects such as stream clean-ups and the incorporation of creation care-based mission trips will simultaneously promote internal theological awareness and external environmental healing. If we Christians acknowledge that the needs of others should take precedence over our desires and that our daily actions can bring the Earth redemption, then the trends noted in Figure 4.1 will be reversed.

---

21   Ripple, W.J., et al. 2017. "World scientists' warning to humanity: A second notice." *Bioscience 67* (12): 1026-1028.

22   ibid. pg. 1026

23   Similar to Wendell Berry, N.T. Write acknowledges that the mindset that technology will bring progress has not been realized, but he adds that Christians, not technology, can bring change. Wright, N.T. 1999. The Millennium Myth: . Louisville, KY: Westminister John Knox. Pg. 39-40

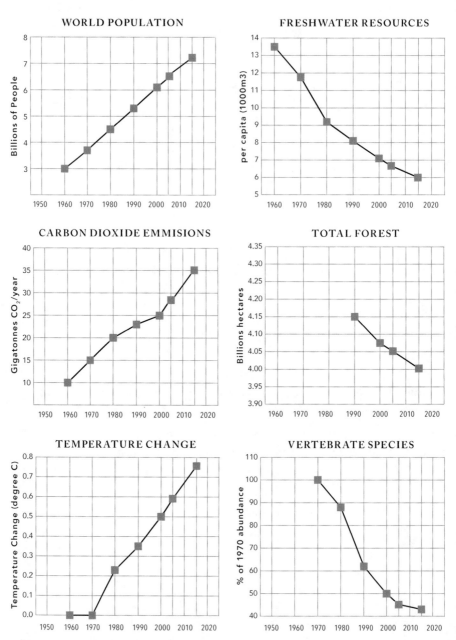

FIGURE 4.1. *Trends since 1960 in world population growth, CO_2 emissions, global temperature change, amount of safe freshwater, total forest area, and vertebrate species abundance. Data from Ripple et al. (2017).[21]*

Table 4.1 presents some specific actions to protect and conserve water, soil, air, and the climate. Some of these items are appropriate for individuals and others are appropriate for churches. Growing up in a small farming community, I understand that these recommendations are nothing new, but tried and true practices used by people that love the land. Unfortunately, many of the small farms of my childhood have been replaced with sprawling subdivisions, and these common-sense practices to conserve the land need to be revisited.

TABLE 4.1. *Examples of Individual and Community Efforts Promoting Creation Care (see endnotes for further explanations).*

Water	Decrease energy use from coal.[1]
	Install rain barrels on downspouts for watering plants.
	Install low-flow shower heads and dual flush toilets.
	Organize and participate in stream and river clean-up events.
	Decrease use of plastics.[2]
	Protect storm drains and roadways from trash and chemical introduction.[3]
	Properly dispose of pharmaceuticals, used motor oil, and pesticides.[4]
Soil	Decrease use of unnatural chemicals.
	Prevent topsoil erosion; stream protection and buffers are particularly important.
	Compost all vegetative and yard waste and use in plantings.
	Plant a garden plot for fresh, organic vegetables (or a small raised garden bed).
	Buy local, organic produce.
Air	Decrease energy use from coal.
	Purchase energy star appliances.
	Use mass transit or drive automobiles with higher MPG ratings.
Climate[5]	Decrease use of fossil fuels.[6]
	Decrease carbon footprint.[7]
	Conduct an energy efficiency audit of your home and church.[8]

Christians should be leaders in following environmentally sustainable practices, such as protecting water, soil, and air is loving God and our neighbor.

Take Home Message

As Christians, we are called to steward creation. Scientists have documented many environmental trends that are harmful and not sustainable, but there are clear steps that Christ followers can take to promote creation care. Indeed, Christians are called to be leaders in this effort.

Questions for Discussion

1. Do you think there is a link between care of the environment and love of God?

2. In Colossians 1: 15-20, Paul discusses God as the creator and Jesus as the reconciler not just of humans but creation as well. Do you view Jesus as not only the redeemer of humanity but also creation?

3. What are some specific steps that you and your church can take to promote creation care?

ENDNOTES

1   The majority of waterways that are imperiled today (for instance, human consumption of fish from lakes is banned, etc.) are so because of mercury toxicity. Whereas mercury is a natural metal, the primary way it gets concentrated in water is due to use of coal. As coal is burned for energy, trace amounts of mercury are released in the air. This mercury then moves into waterways through precipitation, ending up in the bodies of animals where it causes toxicity. Higher concentrations of mercury can be found in older animals because it builds up over an animals' life (this is called bioaccumulation) and in animals higher on the food web (this is called biomagnification). For instance, if a person eats an old, large swordfish that has eaten thousands of smaller fish, the swordfish steak will have harmful, toxic effects of mercury that were once in tons of coal.

2   Plastics are synthetic and long-lived in the environment. Aquatic animals are harmed from plastics due to either consuming them or being exposed to harmful chemicals that are released (e.g., bisphenol A and phthalates are two examples). Many areas of the oceans have more plastic mass than the mass of living organisms. See http://plastic-pollution.org/.

3   Urban and suburban roads have storm drains to help streets from flooding during times of rain. The majority of these storm drains release the water into streams and rivers. Thus, anything that is on the road (e.g., oil, pesticides, trash) will end up in the stream after a rain event.

4   Most communities have "hazardous waste pickup" events that allow proper disposal of substances that end up contaminating water. If hazardous products, including pharmaceutical drugs, are disposed of in the trash, they eventually leach from landfills into water sources causing harm to aquatic animals and humans.

5   Climate differs from weather in terms of time-scale, with climate describing long-term patterns of weather in a particular area, usually more than 30 years. See https://climate.nasa.gov/scientific-consensus/ for the scientific consensus on climate change.

6   While atmospheric CO_2 levels have been higher in the past, such as during the age of dinosaurs, so was temperature. What is different today is the rate of CO_2 and temperature change, which is due to human actions since the industrial revolution. The primary human-caused contributor to climate change is CO_2. When fossil fuels are combusted, CO_2 is released into the atmosphere.

7   See https://www.epa.gov/ghgemissions/household-carbon-footprint-calculator to determine specific steps that you can take to reduce your carbon footprint.

8   Most local power companies will conduct a free home or church energy audit. In addition, see https://www.energy.gov/public-services/homes/home-weatherization/home-energy-audits.

"*Despite all the talk of radical Islam and Christian fundamentalism, the most interesting place in the world from a religious perspective is not the Islamic State or the Bible Belt, but Silicon Valley. That's where hi-tech gurus are brewing for us brave new religions that have little to do with God, and everything to do with technology. They promise all the old prizes — happiness, peace, prosperity and even eternal life—but here on earth with the help of technology, rather than after death with the help of celestial beings.*"

∞∞ YUVAL HARARI*

*Harari, Y.N. 2017. *Homo Deus: A Brief Hisotry of Tomorrow*. New York: HarperCollins Publishers. pg. 356

SESSION 5:

The Future Landscape: Redeeming Truth

FOCAL BIBLE VERSES

∞∞ 1 Corinthians 6: 12   ∞∞ 1 Corinthians 15: 35-58

Introduction

THE FUTURE OF our culture's engagement of science and Christianity is uncertain, but one thing is clear: Christian communities must engage in informed discussion about the interaction of science with our faith. In this session, we will examine one topic emerging as a result of technological progress, transhumanism. After this, a vision for the future of science and Christianity will be given.

Transhumanism

The terms transhumanism and posthumanism refer to the idea that in the near future humans will merge with technology to create a new species. While at first sounding like science fiction, the reality of such merging is already underway and will be an issue that the present generation will face. Science is providing the technological reality to promote the merge, but how Christians should respond is less clear.

Scientific Perspectives

Our species, *Homo sapiens*, evolved on the plains of Africa around 200,000 years before present and began a global migration approximately 100,000 years ago.[1] Fossils and artifacts indicate that this new species of primate was distinct from all other animals on the planet in its unique combination of traits including the ability to vocally communicate, to rapidly modify tools, to transmit information in a means of social learning, to live socially and, quite uniquely, to think symbolically. These traits occurred suddenly in an event referred to as the "mind's big bang," the first cognitive revolution in our species. [2 & 3]

Our species has subtly changed over the past 100,000 years, primarily due to adaptations to different climatic regions, the advent of agriculture, and industrialization combined with globalism. But perhaps the greatest changes are occurring today through technology. Humans in industrialized countries are not under the influence of natural selection, as medical technology prolongs lifespan and agricultural technology produces excessive resources.[4] For example, 100 years ago I would not have survived to have children and pass on my genes; I was born premature and kept alive in an incubator, had appendicitis as an adolescent, and developed type-1 diabetes as a young adult. Simply stated, I would not be alive without medical technology. However, due to technology, I was gifted with the blessing to have three wonderful children. I and others living in the developed world have overcome natural selection through technology.

The past forty years has seen an acceleration in technological progress. It is hard to contemplate life without smart phones and computers and even more difficult to accept that the first Macintosh was not sold until 1984. In recent decades, humans have begun merging their biological bodies with technology.

---

1   Smithsonian National Museum of Natural History. 2018. *What does it mean to be human?* April 5. Accessed April 5, 2018. http://humanorigins.si.edu/.

2   WGBH Educational Foundation & Blue Sky Productions. 2001. *Show 6: The Mind's Big Bang.* Accessed April 5, 2018. http://www.pbs.org/wgbh/evolution/about/show06.html.

3   Harari, Y.N. 2017. *Homo Deus: A Brief Hisotry of Tomorrow.* New York: HarperCollins Publishers.

4   Thus, two of the basic tenants of natural selection are not applicable: (a) overproduction of offspring that can survive and (b) limitation of resources.

For instance, type-1 diabetics utilize artificial pancreases and faulty heart sinoatrial nodes are replaced with artificial pacemakers. Thankfully, such merging of medical technology saves human lives and promotes longevity, again overcoming the rules of natural selection where the environment determines survivability. Artificial organs replace those that fail, and each year there is much progress in this field of regenerative medicine; indeed, there is an entire scientific journal devoted to the topic: The Journal of Artificial Organs. 3-D bioprinters print simpler tissues such as skin for transplantation, and complex organs like the kidney have been artificially printed.[5] Such merging of technology in our body is welcome, as it improves the human condition through therapeutic means, but many non-scientific questions arise when technology is considered for enhancement of our body and improvement of mental processing.

Optimists surmise that in the near future, not only will technology be used for therapeutic purposes but also to enhance cognitive functions and even upload our brain's information to an artificial medium.[6] This merge of mental capacity with machine is expected to be an irreversible change, a time when we will transcend our biological bodies; this is called "the singularity," a term popularized by current Director of Engineering at Google Raymond Kurtzweil. The singularity is expected to be such a radical change that many believe a new species will be created.[7] Kurtzweil is certainly an optimist, believing that the singularity will not only solve health problems but will also overcome poverty, reverse environmental destruction, and provide eternal life.[8]

Is the singularity possible? Many scholars doubt it. Biologists argue that the human brain has approximately 100 billion neurons, and each of these

---

5   National Institute of Biomedical Imaging and Bioengineering. 2018. *Artificial kidney development advances, thanks to collaboration by NIBIB Quantum grantees.* January 16. Accessed April 5, 2018 . https://www.nibib.nih.gov/news-events/newsroom/artificial-kidney-development-advances-thanks-collaboration-nibib-quantum.

6   Kurzweil, R. 2006. *The Singularity is Near: When Humans Transcend Biology.* Penguin Books.

7   *Homo cyberneticus, Techno sapiens,* and *Homo deus* have been proposed for the new species to be created from the merging of *Homo sapiens* with technology.

8   Kurtzweil, R. 2013. "Progress and relinquishment." In *The Transhumanist Reader,* edited by Max More and Natasha Vita-More, 451-453. Chichester, West Sussex: John Wiley & Sons.

neurons has between 1000 and 10,000 connections (called synapses) with other neurons,[9] a feat that would seem to surpass even the most optimistic computer science estimates. Additionally, psychologists and sociologists posit that the human learning and integration go well beyond simple data transfer.[10] Are humans just a product of physical synapses, data input, and data output?

That said, the pursuit of the singularity is ongoing.[11] If calculus can be downloaded into a human brain or a Google search conducted internally, what implications does this have for our humanity? Should cognitive manipulation be attempted? These questions are not scientific, and need to be addressed by faith communities.[12]

Christian Perspectives

Questions raised from the scientific reality of merging our species with technology have no clear answers, and there are two lines of thought on how Christians should respond: cautious embracing or rejection.

CAUTIOUS EMBRACING

Singularity optimists support a cautious embracing of the singularity. Christian ethicist Brent Waters states that "when the postmodern emphasis… is joined with this cybernetic vision, there is no real compelling reason why radically posthuman transformation should not be pursued"[13] and theologian Calvin Mercer summarizes "there is no theological reason to reject and resist

9   Chudler, E. n.d. *Brain Facts and Figures.* Accessed April 24, 2018. https://faculty.washington.edu/chudler/facts.html.

10   see Barrett, J. 2011. *Cognitive Science, Religion, and Theology: From Human Minds to Divine Minds.* West Conshohocken, PA: Templeton Press.

11   Max, D.T. 2017. "How humans are shaping our own evolution." *National Geographic,* April.

12   The Vatican began considering the implications of transhumanism in 2018. See Our Sunday Visitor. 2018. *The Church wrestles with transhumanism.* February 21. Accessed April 9, 2018.

13   Waters, T. 2006. *From Human to Posthuman: Christian Theology and Technology in a Postmodern World.* New York: Routledge Press. pg. x.

the transhumanism/posthumanism vision…"[14] These arguments are based not only on the potential of a cybernetic eternal existence, but also a permanent improved bodily existence via technology. This would bring the theology of bodily resurrection into physical reality, and potentially fulfill Paul's explanation in 1 Corinthians of the splendor of our resurrected, imperishable heavenly bodies:

> But someone will ask, "How are the dead raised? With what kind of body will they come?" How foolish! What you sow does not come to life unless it dies. When you sow, you do not plant the body that will be, but just a seed, perhaps of wheat or of something else. But God gives it a body as he has determined, and to each kind of seed he gives its own body. Not all flesh is the same: People have one kind of flesh, animals have another, birds another and fish another. There are also heavenly bodies and there are earthly bodies; but the splendor of the heavenly bodies is one kind, and the splendor of the earthly bodies is another. The sun has one kind of splendor, the moon another and the stars another; and star differs from star in splendor.
>
> So will it be with the resurrection of the dead. The body that is sown is perishable, it is raised imperishable; it is sown in dishonor, it is raised in glory; it is sown in weakness, it is raised in power; it is sown a natural body, it is raised a spiritual body.
>
> If there is a natural body, there is also a spiritual body. So it is written: "The first man Adam became a living being"; the last Adam, a life-giving spirit. The spiritual did not come first, but the natural, and after that the spiritual. The first man was of the dust of the earth; the second man is of heaven. As was the earthly man, so are those who are of the earth; and as is the heavenly man, so also are those who are of heaven. And just as we have borne the image of the earthly man, so shall we bear the image of the heavenly man.

---

14   Mercer, C. 2015. "Bodies and persons: Theological reflections on transhumanism." *Dialog: A Journal of Theology*, pg. 31

I declare to you, brothers and sisters, that flesh and blood cannot inherit the kingdom of God, nor does the perishable inherit the imperishable. Listen, I tell you a mystery: We will not all sleep, but we will all be changed— in a flash, in the twinkling of an eye, at the last trumpet. For the trumpet will sound, the dead will be raised imperishable, and we will be changed. For the perishable must clothe itself with the imperishable, and the mortal with immortality. When the perishable has been clothed with the imperishable, and the mortal with immortality, then the saying that is written will come true: "Death has been swallowed up in victory."

"Where, O death, is your victory?
Where, O death, is your sting?"

The sting of death is sin, and the power of sin is the law. But thanks be to God! He gives us the victory through our Lord Jesus Christ.

Therefore, my dear brothers and sisters, stand firm. Let nothing move you. Always give yourselves fully to the work of the Lord, because you know that your labor in the Lord is not in vain.

∞∞∞ 1 Corinthians 15: 35-58

Some theologians take an extremely optimistic view of the singularity, viewing it as the final human unification with God. One of the early thinkers that has influenced this mindset is Jesuit Priest Teilhard de Chardin, a pious Christian and preeminent paleontologist in the early 1900s. de Chardin wrote of the unifying nature of all truths in Christ, which he termed "the Omega Point."[15] This Omega Point idea posits that everything in the universe, spiritual and material, will eventually merge with Christ in a divine unification. After considering the extremely puzzling relationship between spirit and matter, Teilhard came to see God in everything, a concept he called the divine milieu, and illustrated that evolution, including human evolution, can be a window to better see and understand God.

---

15   de Chardin, P.T. 1968. *Science and Christ*. New York: Harper & Row Publisher.

"Let us establish ourselves in the divine milieu. There we shall find ourselves where the soul is most deep and where matter is most dense. There we shall discover, where all its beauties flow together, the ultra-vital, the ultra-sensitive, the ultra-active point of the universe. And, at the same time, we shall feel the plentitude of our powers of action and adoration effortlessly ordered within our deepest selves."[16]

During Teilhard's life, technology had not advanced enough to foresee the singularity, but if he were alive today, de Chardin would likely view transhumanism as the culmination of unification with God. However, many view Teilhard's ideas as dangerous,[17] and there is much opposition to the pursuit of the singularity.

REJECTION

Those that reject supporting the singularity cite opposition from theological (problems of personhood being defined by the physical body), philosophical (uploaded information does not equate with personhood), and ethical (social justice) grounds.[18] Additionally, the promise of transhumanism has come to replace religious faith for some former Christians,[19] and thus there is a worry that even if the singularity is a century away, the vitality of Christianity will suffer from the awareness of and anticipation of our permanent merge with technology. There are early signs that this is the case in Europe, where the majority of religiously unaffiliated individuals state that science makes religion unnecessary.[20]

---

16   de Chardin, P.T. 1960. *The Divine Milieu*. New York: Harper Perrennial Press. Pg. 87

17   Sacred Congregation of the Holy Office. 1981. *Warning regarding the writings of father Teilhard de Chardin*. Accessed June 27, 2018. https://www.catholicculture.org/culture/library/view.cfm?id=3160.

18   Peters, T. 2006. *Anticipating Omega: Science, Faith, and Our Ultimate Future* . Gottingen, Germany: Vandenhoeck & Ruprecht.

19   O'Bieblyn, M. 2017. *God in the machine: my strage journey into transhumanism*. April 18. Accessed April 9, 2018. https://www.theguardian.com/technology/2017/apr/18/god-in-the-machine-my-strange-journey-into-transhumanism.

20   Pew Research Center. 2018. *Being Christian in Western Europe*. May 29. Accessed June 13, 2018. http://www.pewforum.org/2018/05/29/being-christian-in-western-europe/.

Scriptures such as 1 Corinthians 6: 12 can be used to justify the rejection of transhumanism. Whereas the original context of this verse was Paul's admonition against sexual immorality, the general sentiment can be used as a warning against many technological advances of modern society including the potential of merging technology with our bodies for cognitive enhancement and technological eternal life.

> Everything is permissible for me" – but not everything is beneficial.
> Everything is permissible for me"—but I will not be mastered by anything.
>
> ∞∞∞ 1 Corinthians 6: 12

Besides scriptural warnings, there are many other reasons for Christians to reject transhumanism. The merging of our cognitive functions for enhancement purposes implies being mastered by the technology. In addition, it is arrogant and sinful to believe that we can save ourselves from death. One of the fundamental Christian beliefs is that humans are sinful, need saving by God, and are redeemed through belief in Christ. To believe that we can save ourselves through technology is sinful, and this is the fundamental purpose of the singularity.[21] Indeed, believing that technology is our savior is modern-day idolatry.

Writer and cultural critic Wendell Berry has a wonderful quote that reflects the arrogance in such idolatry:

> "The great question that hovers over this issue, one that we have dealt with mainly by indifference, is the question of what people are *for*. …Is the obsolescence of human beings now our social goal? One would conclude so from our… rush toward mechanization, automation, and computerization."[22]

What are people for? Are we here to enhance our cognition through technology or through our dependence on our creator? Are we alive today to

---

21   Hoskins, James. 2017. *Transhumanism and Christian Orthodoxy: Where Do We Draw the Line?* April 20. Accessed June 12, 2018. https://christandpopculture.com/transhumanism-christian-orthodoxy-draw-line/.

22   Berry, W. 2010. *What Are People For?* Second. Berkeley, CA: Counterpoint Press. pg. 125

promote eternal existence through technology or through our relationship with God? These are the questions that all faith communities must directly address.

The Future of Science and Christianity

The future of science and Christianity is uncertain, but there are signs that these two ways of knowing will both be valued by future generations. First, the perception that scientists are anti-religious is being dispelled.[23] Science today is focused completely on *logos*, and *logos* questions are distinct from those of *mythos* (see Session 1). Second, faith communities are beginning to recognize the importance in acknowledging the need for discussion of science.[24] During this time-period of human history when science and technological advances are a dominant way of knowing, churches are recognizing the fruitful nature of engaging both *mythos* and *logos*. Third, and most importantly, the majority of young Christians embrace the need for both science and faith. This third point needs clarification.

It is true that young people today are less likely to be religious than in times past. For instance, of all age groups surveyed, the 18-29 group are least likely to believe in God (51% reported that they are absolutely certain that God exists), and 35% of U.S. 18 to 29-year-olds claim to be religiously unaffiliated, termed the "nones" because they select the "none" box on queries about their religious affiliation.[25] That said, it is my perception that young people that

---

23 For example, see Ecklund, E. 2017. "The march for science isn't anti-religion. Most scientists aren't either." *Christianity Today*, April 24. and PBS. 2001. *Evolution and Religion: What about God?* Accessed June 28, 2018. http://www.pbs.org/wgbh/evolution/religion/index.html.

24 For example, many protestant denominations are sponsoring workshops on topics on evolution and creation care, and the Catholic church actively acknowledges the importance of science (see http://www.newadvent.org/cathen/13598b.htm). The John Templeton Foundation summarizes: "Contrary to polarized media reports covering religious attitudes toward science, initial interview data from the Religious Understandings of Science study reveals that many religious people think that their faith can be harmonious with science and share narratives about the positive intersections between belief and science." https://www.templeton.org/grant/religious-understandings-of-science

25 Pew Research Center. 2014. *Religious Landscape Study.* May 30. Accessed June 27, 2018. http://www.pewforum.org/religious-landscape-study/age-distribution/.

identify as Christians are more likely embrace both science and faith, both *logos* and *mythos*. At a time when science is viewed as the primary universal truth, young Christians are perfectly poised to bring hope and purpose to the world. For the sake of the local church, I hope this is true.

Take Home Message

We live at a unique time in human history, a time when science is equated with technology and technological advances are influencing human evolution. Scientific advances suggest that in the near future human cognition will be merged with technology, perhaps even leading to a new species, a "transhuman." This is one of the many complex scientific issues that Christians need to address. It is hoped that in doing so, both *logos* and *mythos* ways of knowing will be revitalized, and all truth will be redeemed.

Questions for Discussion

1. After considering the potential reality of transhumanism in the near future, do you reject or cautiously embrace the singularity? Explain.

2. Even those that support transhumanism believe we should proceed with caution. If you do believe in cautious embracing, what are some examples of implications that should be avoided? In other words, where should we be most cautious?

3. Many people today question the importance of organized religion (i.e. churches), and some of this is based on the perceived conflict between science and Christianity. How can your faith community demonstrate that truths found from both science and Christianity are vitally important?

About the Author

DR. DREW CRAIN is Professor of Biology at Maryville College in East Tennessee. Passionate about his undergraduate students, Drew has won the "Teacher of the Year" award several times and can often be found teaching and leading hikes in the Great Smoky Mountains National Park. Dr. Crain's main area of research is focused on environmental health, but recently his scholarly activities have turned to the compatibility of science and Christianity. Drew is active in his local church, where he has served as elder, pastoral council member, and Bible study teacher for the past 20 years.